PLANET OF SECRETS

Contents

by Sally Odgers
illustrated by Georgina Thomas

SCHOLASTIC

THE ARKIES

Reading Manga: What is it?

The Japanese word 'manga' has been used for nearly 200 years. It means whimsical pictures (man = whimsical, ga = pictures).

Today, manga is a label for Japanese-style graphic novels, comic books and animated movies (also called anime). What's the difference between a graphic novel and a comic book? The answer is in your hands. Graphic novels are usually quality productions, some-times run to hundreds of pages, and often cover serious subjects. Many Japanese manga focus on topics like the environment, the law, science, history – you name it.

Manga don't all look exactly the same, but they have some things in common:

Big Eyes

Oversized
Expressions

Fast Action

Reading Manga:
How to Follow

Each page of a graphic novel is divided into boxes called panels. You follow the panels from left to right and top to bottom, like this:

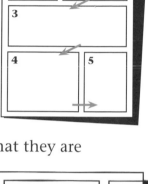

Each panel is like a paragraph in a regular book. It shows you where the characters are, and what they are doing, saying and thinking.

Some panels include a little box at the top (or the bottom), giving you information about what's going on. These are called captions.

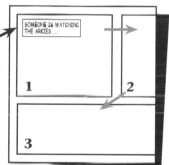

SOMEONE IS WATCHING THE ARKIES ...

DID YOU KNOW?

Traditional Japanese manga look a little different. That's because in Japan, people read from right to left. Japanese manga is read like this:

It's easier than it looks!

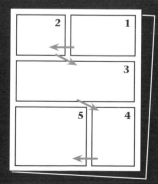

Reading Manga: Who's talking?

Speech balloons tell you who is speaking, what they're saying, and how.

Sometimes the lettering changes, to tell you which words are most important. These words might appear in **BOLD** or LARGE TYPE or in *ITALICS*.

Sometimes a punctuation point is enough to explain what's going on.

And how would you show an alien language? Maybe like this:

Reading Manga: What's that sound?

When you read speech bubbles, you hear manga characters' voices inside your head. There's a way to hear the background noises too – the rumble of thunder, the ringing of a telephone, the crack of a stick underfoot.

Manga artists represent sound effects (or SFX) by placing words over the panels, using lettering to suit each particular sound. It looks like this:

Scary sound

Mechanical sound

Quiet sound

DID YOU KNOW?

Japanese manga SFX are very precise. For example, *bicha bicha* means small splash, *bashan* is a medium splash, and *zaban* is a very big splash. There's even an SFX for total silence: *shiin*.

SFX are used to show emotions as well. The word *unzori* placed next to a character tells you they're feeling bored. If it was *moji moji* they'd be feeling shy, and *shobo shobo* indicates sadness.

Reading Manga:
What's that look on your face?

Manga characters have exaggerated expressions, to help you understand what they're feeling. The first feature everyone notices is the eyes, which may be wide open in:

Shock

Fear

Hope

Closed eyes can mean:

Laughter

Sadness

Noses and chins are more difficult to spot (some characters have no nose at all). This reflects the Japanese preference for delicate features. In manga, big noses and chins are kept for the bad guys.

Reading Manga:

What's that look on your face?

Just like manga characters' eyes, manga mouths are either huge or tiny. A big, wide-open mouth indicates:

Fear   Anger   Happiness

A character with a little mouth may be feeling:

Sad   Thoughtful   Shy

You can also tell a lot about manga characters from the crazy colour or style of their hair. For example, blue hair means the character has lots of energy, while orange hair equals determination (and sometimes a fiery temper). Wild, spiky hairstyles show the character is adventurous.

Characters

Singer

Gentle Singer can sense the mind of any living being, and communicate by thought alone. She understands many languages.

Lyam

Science whiz Lyam can tell the Arkies everything they need to know about alien plant and animal life – and then some.

Merlinna

Merlinna is always ready for a battle. She's an expert with weapons – including her naturally piercing screech.

Pace

Pace is a practical guy with a very practical skill – he can communicate with electronic equipment. He and Singer are special friends.

EarthNet

Tench and Farla are EarthNet agents who trail the *Ark3*. They want to capture the Arkies and return them to Earth.

Tench   Farla

ARK3 HAS LANDED, BUT THE ARKIES ARE NOT THE FIRST TO VISIT THIS PLANET. THE SHIPBRAIN ARKMA EXPLAINS THE SITUATION ...

ALERT! A SHIP CALLED GREENFIELDS LANDED HERE LONG AGO.

SO IT'S ALREADY BEEN EXPLORED?

MY RECORDS SHOW THE SHIP TOUCHED DOWN AND LEFT IMMEDIATELY.

THEY LEFT SOMETHING BEHIND.

- 11 -

- 14 -

chapter 3 : Strangers Are Bad

THE ARKIES LEAP TO DEFEND HEYA.

STOP IT! WE'LL COME WITH YOU.

IT'S OK, HEYA. WE WON'T LET HIM HURT YOU.

SIR HAS HAD ENOUGH.

ENOUGH!

YOU! YOU ARE THE BAD STRANGERS. HEYA KNOWS IT. GUARDS!

LATER, EVERYTHING HAS BEEN EXPLAINED.

GOODBYE MY DEARS, AND THANK YOU. HEYA AND HER FRIENDS WILL TAKE YOU BACK TO YOUR ARKMA.

WHAT ABOUT EARTHNET?

WE'LL KEEP THEM HERE UNTIL YOU GET SAFELY AWAY.

Arkies Teenagers who seek out new Settlement-Ready planets.

Ark3 The Arkies' space craft.

ArkMa The electronic mind that flies *Ark3*. A shipbrain.

Didgies Indigenous inhabitants of a planet.

EarthNet An organisation that wants to send the Arkies home.

MatCon A matter converter, used to convert matter into useful objects.

S-R (Settlement-Ready) Planets with oxygen, water, vegetation, metal and no intelligent didgies.

Tangle-line A weapon that tangles around arms or legs, and stings but does not injure.